GUSTAV HOLS[T]

T0084606

SAVITR[I]

By arrangement with J. Curwen & Sons Ltd. and G. & I. Holst Ltd.
Foreword by Imogen Holst

Ernst Eulenburg Ltd
London · Mainz · Madrid · New York · Paris · Tokyo · Toronto · Zürich

GUSTAV HOLST
Sāvitri

It was in the late eighteen-nineties that Holst began studying Sanskrit. His first Indian opera was the unpublished, unperformed, extravagantly conceived three-act *Sita* (1900-6) which he afterwards referred to as 'good old Wagnerian bawling'. He wrote *Sāvitri* two years later in 1908, and finished work on the full score early in 1909. The simplicity and economy of this short *opera di camera* must have seemed startling at that time. The sentence in the Composer's Note, saying 'no curtain is necessary', can be accepted as a matter of course in the late twentieth century, but audiences of fifty years ago were unprepared for the challenge of the opening phrase, when, without warning, the distant voice of unseen Death is heard in the darkness.

The libretto is Holst's own version of an episode from the Sanskrit Mahābhārata. Sāvitri, the wife of a woodman, Satyavān, is waiting for him to return from the forest when she hears the words of Death: 'I come for thy husband.' When Satyavān enters, he sees that she is frightened, and tells her that she is under the spell of Māyā (Illusion). He hears a stranger approaching and tries to raise his axe, but falls lifeless to the ground. Death appears, and Sāvitri welcomes him in spite of her distress, greeting him as 'the Just One'. Death is so moved that he promises to grant her anything she asks except the life of her husband. She asks for her own life in its fullness, and when Death agrees she triumphantly proves to him that her life would be impossible without Satyavān. Death realizes that he has been defeated, and returns alone to his Kingdom 'where men dream that they are dead, for even Death is Māyā'. Satyavān wakes to find Sāvitri's arms round him, and she tells him that one of the Holy Ones has visited them and blessed them.

Sāvitri was first performed on 5 December 1916 at Wellington Hall, St John's Wood, by students of the London School of Opera, conducted by Hermann Grunebaum. During the preliminary rehearsals of the off-stage chorus, which was at first intended for mixed voices, the tenor line always sounded unsatisfactory, and Grunebaum suggested that Holst should rewrite the choral parts for women's voices. This change was beautifully effective, and Holst never forgot his gratitude for Grunebaum's advice. The first public performance was on 23 June 1921 at the Lyric Theatre, Hammersmith, with Steuart Wilson (Satyavān), Dorothy Silk (Sāvitri) and Clive Carey (Death), conducted by Arthur Bliss: the producer was Clive Carey, and the costumes were designed and the scenery supervised by C. Lovat Fraser. This was the first occasion on which Dorothy Silk sang Holst's music in public. From then onwards, she was his chosen soprano soloist.

He made several small alterations to the score in the autumn of 1921, as the result of listening to performances, and the work was published in 1923 by Goodwin and Tabb Ltd. and subsequently brought out by J. Curwen & Sons Ltd. in 1924.

During the years following Holst's death in 1934 the opera was seldom performed except by music students and by a few adventurous amateur operatic societies. The printed full score was no longer on sale, and anyone wishing to study it had to be content with a hired copy. By the nineteen-sixties, however, there was a remarkable increase of interest in Holst's music. Listeners were willing to explore his early works without worrying too much about discrepancies of style. In *Sāvitri*, the occasional romantic passages no longer stood out as uncomfortable reminders of his immature struggles, and the impressive strength of the opera was recognized.

In 1973 the publishers brought out a revised edition of the full score, correcting the misprints and making the marginal lay-out of the two string quartets easier to read. It is the 1973 publication which forms the basis of this miniature score, with the following additional details:
Flutes, bar 153: *dim.* has been deleted.
Cellos and basses, bar 432: the natural has been added to E.

The autograph manuscript of the full score is in the Bodleian Library: MS Don.c.3. It is reproduced in Volume I of the *Collected Facsimile Edition* of Holst's works published by Faber Music Ltd.

Imogen Holst 1976

Composer's Note

This piece is intended for performance in the open air, or else in a small building.

When performed out of doors there should be a long avenue or path through a wood in the centre of the scene.

When a Curtain is used, it should be raised before the voice of Death is heard.

No Curtain, however, is necessary.

The Orchestra consists of two string quartets, a contrabass, two flutes, and an English Horn.

There is also a hidden chorus of female voices. They are to sing throughout to the sound of 'u' in 'sun'.

Conductor, Chorus, and Orchestra are to be invisible to the Audience.

If a Prelude is required, the Composer suggests his 'Hymn of the Travellers' from Choral Hymns from the Rig Veda, Set III, *for female voices and harp (published by Stainer & Bell).*

Note to the Revised Edition

Holst's own written directions on the first page of the score show that he had clear ideas about the production of the opera. He wished it to be as simple as possible, with no elaborate scenery and with only a few carefully controlled gestures. He left no suggestions for the design of the costumes, but he always insisted that the figure of Death should be dignified and godlike, with nothing in the least frightening or grotesque in the characterisation.

The dramatic atmosphere of a stage production of Sāvitri *can owe a great deal to the right balance of texture in the music. The chorus should be as distant as possible, which may mean that a sub-conductor will be needed. And it is very important to keep to the correct number of strings; Holst would never have allowed them to be augmented beyond the two string quartets and double bass for which the music was written.*

I.H.

GUSTAV HOLST

Sāvitri

Holst begann mit seinen Sanskritstudien gegen Ende der neunziger Jahre des letzten Jahrhunderts. *Sita* (1900-6), seine erste Oper über indische Themen in drei Akten, war in ihrer Konzeption masslos. Sie blieb unveröffentlicht und ist nie aufgeführt worden. Wenn Holst sie später erwähnte, sprach er von ihr als einem ‚echten, alten wagnerischen Gebrüll'. *Sāvitri* schrieb er zwei Jahre später, 1908, und Anfang 1909 vollendete er die Partitur. Die einfache und sparsame Anlage dieser kurzen *opera di camera* muss damals als äusserst überraschend angesehen worden sein. Der Satz in den Anmerkungen des Komponisten, in dem es heisst, ‚ein Vorhang ist nicht nötig', kann im späteren zwanzigsten Jahrhundert als selbstverständlich angenommen werden, aber vor fünfzig Jahren war das Publikum den Ansprüchen, die im Anfang der Oper liegen, wenn die Stimme des unsichtbaren Todes unerwartet im Dunkeln aus der Ferne klingt, nicht gewachsen.

Das Textbuch ist Holsts eigene Fassung einer Geschichte aus dem epischen Gedicht im Sanskrit, Mahābhārata. Sāvitri, die Frau des Holzfällers Satyavān, hört, während sie auf die Rückkehr ihres Mannes aus dem Wald wartet, die vom Tod gesprochenen Worte: „Ich komme, um deinen Mann zu holen." Satyavān bemerkt beim Auftritt, dass sie verängstigt ist und erklärt ihr, sie stehe im Banne der Māyā (Täuschung). Wie er das Näherkommen eines Fremden hört, versucht er seine Axt zu heben, fällt aber leblos zu Boden. Der Tod tritt auf. Sāvitri heisst ihn trotz ihres Kummers willkommen und begrüsst ihn als ‚den Gerechten'. Der Tod ist so gerührt davon, dass er ihr die Erfüllung eines Wunsches, was es auch sei, nur nicht die Wiederbelebung ihres Mannes, verspricht. Sie wünscht sich ihr eigenes Leben in all seiner Fülle. Der Tod gewährt es ihr, worauf sie ihm triumphierend beweist, dass ihr Leben ohne Satyavān nicht möglich ist. Der Tod gibt sich geschlagen und kehrt allein in sein Reich zurück, ‚in welchem der Mensch träumt, dass er tot ist, denn selbst der Tod ist Māyā.' Satyavān erwacht in Sāvitris Armen, und sie erzählt ihm, einer der Heiligen habe sie aufgesucht und gesegnet.

Sāvitri wurde erstmalig am 5. Dezember 1916 in der Wellington Hall in St. John's Wood, London, von Studenten der London Opera School, unter der Leitung von Hermann Grunebaum, aufgeführt. Während der ersten Proben mit dem Chor hinter der Bühne, der zuerst gemischten Stimmen zugedacht war, klang der Tenor stets wenig zufriedenstellend, worauf Grunebaum Holst den Vorschlag machte, die Stimmen für Frauenchor umzuschreiben. Diese Änderung erwies sich als ebenso schön wie wirkungsvoll, und Holst blieb Grunebaum für seinen Rat zeitlebens dankbar. Die erste öffentliche Aufführung fand am 23. Juni 1921 im Lyric Theatre in Hammersmith, London, mit Steuart Wilson (Satyavān), Dorothy Silk (Sāvitri) und Clive Carey (der Tod), unter der Leitung von Arthur Bliss statt. Clive Carey besorgte die Inszenierung, und die Kostüme wurden von C. Lovat Fraser entworfen, der auch bei der Arbeit am Bühnenbild die Aufsicht führte. Bei dieser Gelegenheit sang Dorothy Silk zum ersten Mal in einem Werk von Holst in der Öffentlichkeit. Sie wurde dann stets seine erste Wahl als Solosopran.

Auf Grund der von ihm gehörten Aufführungen machte er im Herbst 1921 einige geringfügige Änderungen in der Partitur. Das Werke wurde 1923 von Goodwin and Tabb Ltd. verlegt und dann 1924 von J. Curwen & Sons Ltd. herausgegeben.

In den Jahren, die auf Holsts Tod im Jahre 1934 folgten, wurde die Oper, ausser von Musikstudenten oder einigen unternehmungslustigen Opernensembles von Dilettanten, selten aufgeführt. Die gedruckte Partitur war nicht mehr käuflich zu erwerben. Wer sie studieren wollte, musste sich mit einer gegen Gebühr geliehenen Partitur zufrieden geben. Jedoch schon vor den sechziger Jahren dieses Jahrhunderts machte sich eine wesentliche Zunahme im Interesse an Holsts Musik bemerkbar. Die Zuhörerschaft zeigte sich nun gewillt, seine frühen Werke zu ergründen, ohne sich dabei zu sehr um stilistische Uneinheitlichkeiten zu kümmern. Die gelegentlichen romantischen Passagen in *Sāvitri* wurden nicht mehr als störende Erinnerung an seine Entwicklungskämpfe empfunden, und die eindrucksvolle Kraft der Oper wurde allgemein anerkannt.

In Jahre 1973 gaben die Verleger eine revidierte Ausgabe der Partitur heraus, in der die Druckfehler berichtigt, und das Randbild der Notensysteme für die beiden Streichquartette leichter lesbar waren. Auf dieser Ausgabe des Jahres 1973 beruht die vorliegende Studienpartitur, abgesehen von den folgenden Zusätzen:
Takt 153, Flöten: *dim* wurde gestrichen.
Takt 432, Celli und Bässe: ein Auflösungszeichen ist vor dem E hinzugefügt worden.

Das Autograph der Partitur befindet sich in der Bodleian Library in Oxford unter der Bezeichnung: MS Don.c.3. Es wurde im ersten Band der *Collected Facsimile Edition* der Werke Holsts, von Faber Music Ltd. veröffentlicht, reproduziert.

Imogen Holst 1976
Deutsche Übersetzung Stefan de Haan

Anmerkungen des Komponisten

Dieses Stück ist für eine Aufführung im Freien oder in einem kleinen Gebäude gedacht.

Wenn es im Freien aufgeführt wird, sollte sich in der Mitte der Bühne eine lange Allee oder ein langer Pfad durch einen Wald befinden.

Wenn ein Vorhang verwendet wird, sollte er geöffnet werden, bevor man die Stimme des Todes hört.

Ein Vorhang ist jedoch nicht nötig.

Die Besetzung des Orchesters besteht aus zwei Streichquartetten, einem Kontrabass, zwei Flöten und einem Englischhorn.

Ausserdem enthält die Besetzung der Stimmen einen unsichtbaren Chor von Frauenstimmen, der durchweg auf dem Vokal 'a' (wie das englische u im Wort sun) zu singen hat.

Dirigent, Chor und Orchester sollen dem Publikum unsichtbar bleiben.

Sollte ein Vorspiel benötigt werden, so schlägt der Komponist seine ‚Hymn of the Travellers' aus den Choral Hymns from the Rig Veda, dritter Teil, für Frauenstimmen und Harfe (verlegt von Stainer & Bell) vor.

Anmerkungen zur revidierten Ausgabe

Die von Holst selbst geschriebenen Anweisungen auf der ersten Seite der Partitur beweisen, dass er von der Inszenierung der Oper eine genaue Vorstellung gehabt hat. Er hatte den Wunsch, sie so einfach wie möglich zu gestalten, ohne komplizierte Bühnenbilder, und mit nur wenigen, beherrschten Gesten. Für den Entwurf der Kostüme hat er keine Vorschläge gemacht, aber er hat stets darauf bestanden, dass die Figur des Todes würdevoll und im Sinne eines Gottes gespielt werden sollte, sowie ohne jede Spur von etwas Erschreckendem oder Grotesken in der Charakterisierung.

Die dramatische Stimmung einer Aufführung auf der Bühne kann unter Umständen sehr von der ausgewogenen Struktur der Musik abhängig sein. Der Chor sollte so entfernt wie möglich klingen, woraus sich ergeben mag, dass ein Hilfsdirigent benötigt wird. Es ist ausserdem höchst wichtig, sich an die korrekte Anzahl von Streichern zu halten. Holst hätte es nie zugelassen, dass die Besetzung über die zwei Streichquartette und den Kontrabass, hinaus, für welche die Musik geschrieben wurde, erweitert würde.

I.H.

Characters:

SATYAVĀN	(A Woodman)	*Tenor*
SĀVITRI	(His Wife)	*Soprano*
DEATH		*Bass*

CHORUS of female voices

Orchestra:

2 Flutes
English Horn
2 String Quartets
Double Bass

Scene: A Wood at Evening

Duration: 30 minutes.

SĀVITRI

An Episode from the Mahābharata

Revised edition © 1973 by J. Curwen & Sons Ltd.

6

8

*Holst did not repeat accidentals after a dotted bar line: they always apply throughout the bar.

Säv. robe Thou art en _ shroud _ ed in my love. With my song I weave a

spell. E _ vil pow'rs may not ap _ proach within the hear _ ing of my voice On _ ly the

D. faces are the sufferers thou hast comforted, The voices are the sweet words thou hast spoken, the air

D. is made holy by thy love Being with thee is being in Paradise. With thee the

D. gods themselves may dwell.

Săv. Then enter Lord, dwell with me. What better fate befalleth than being with the Holy ones.

D. That may not be,

Animato

D. I am he who leadeth men onward. Yet ere I go, To thee who dost not shrink from me. Who badest me welcome

Agitato

Săv. O

D. I will grant a boon. A boon for thyself, Ask naught for Satyävän My breath hath chilled his heart.

Agitato

23

_ glo _ ri _ ous wo _ _ _ _ man Take the gift thou hast asked Life is thine _ in all its

Sat _ ya _ vân   on _ ly   can   teach   me the song___   can

Säv. o - pen the gate to my path of flow'rs___ The path of a wo_man's

Poco animato

Away, Death, back to thy kingdom. A.

XXVIII   (Death shrinks back)

Säv.   lone must thou tra_vel   true to thy word.

CHORUS.

Fl.

E.H.

A

Viol.I.

Viol.II.

Vla.

Cel.

B

Viol.I.

Viol.II.

Vla.

Cel.

Basso.

XXVIII

XXX Andante

Sat. Mâ.ya had seized me. I was her slave. Now hath she fléd. Nought remains but thou and thy

XXXAndante

Sâv. Without thee I am as the dead, A word without meaning, Fire without

Sat. love, Thou a.lone art free from Mâ.ya, Thou alone art real